FUN

SEA CREATURES

by Jim Razzi
illustrations by Jim Tomasewski

SCHOLASTIC INC.
New York Toronto London Auckland Sydney

ISBN 0-590-40785-6

12 11 10 9 8 7 6 5 4 3 2   1 2 3/9

Printed in the U.S.A.   23
First Scholastic printing, January 1988.

A-Mazing Shark

Find your way in and out of this dangerous shark maze without crossing a line.

Fishy Spelling

The picture below is a kind of secret code.
To break the code, cover up the picture of the fish with
a piece of paper, but do not cover the letters.
Hold the paper straight so that the edge touches the
dotted line. Now, slowly slide the paper to your right.
Every time you come to a black fish — stop! Write
down the letter that's on the same line as the black fish.
What do the eight letters spell? (Hint: It's a popular pet.)

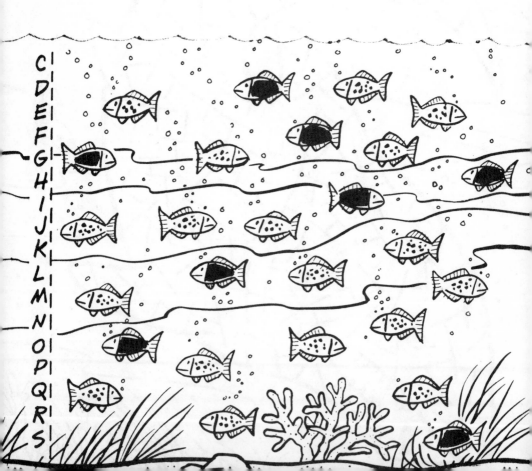

A Surprise Catch

This fisherman has caught something in his net. To see what it is, just hold this page up to a strong light.

What's going on here? Turn to page 5 to find
out.

Sea Turtle Tic-Tac-Toe

To play this game, you must first cut out these eight turtles. Then cut out the board below. The directions for the game are on the back of the board.

Sea Turtle Tic-Tac-Toe

Sea Turtle Tic-Tac-Toe

You can play this game with a friend. One of you takes the white-shelled turtles, the other gets the black-shelled turtles.

The object of the game is to see who can be first to place his turtles four in a row on the playing board. The row can be UP, DOWN, or DIAGONAL, just as in Tic-Tac-Toe.

Take turns placing a turtle on a square, trying to block the other player from getting four in a row. If you both put down all your turtles and no one wins, take turns moving one square in any direction until someone gets four in a row.

Sea Horse Bookmarks

Before making these bookmarks, see the instructions on the next page.

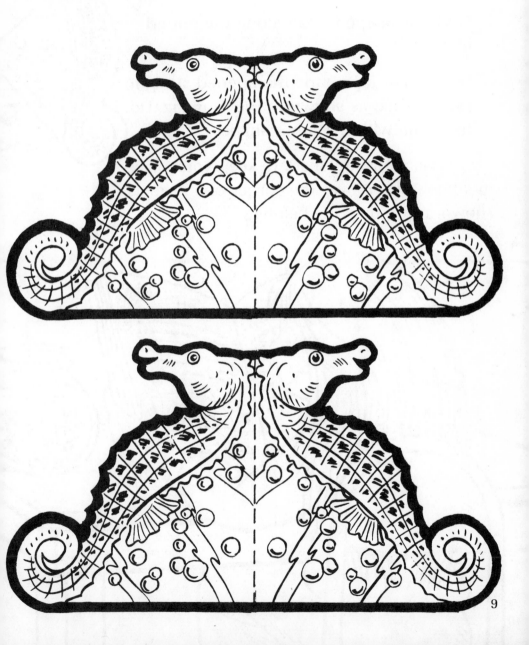

Instructions for Sea Horse Bookmarks

1. Cut out the shapes on page 9 along the black outline.

2. Fold one shape in half along the dotted line.

3. Using clear tape, tape the opened straight sides closed as shown in the drawing. Do the same with the other shape.

   To use your bookmark to keep your place in a book, slip it over the corner of a page as shown in the drawing below.

Draw a Snail — Fast!

Here's a fast way to draw a snail.

Just put a cellophane tape holder on a piece of paper and draw around it, as shown in drawings A and B. Now fill in some lines for the shell and draw a face, as shown in drawing C. It works every time.

Silly Sea Questions

Why did the cowboy go swimming with his boots on?

He wanted to ride a sea horse.

What kind of fish do pilots eat?

Flying fish.

What kind of cats can breathe underwater?

Octo-pusses.

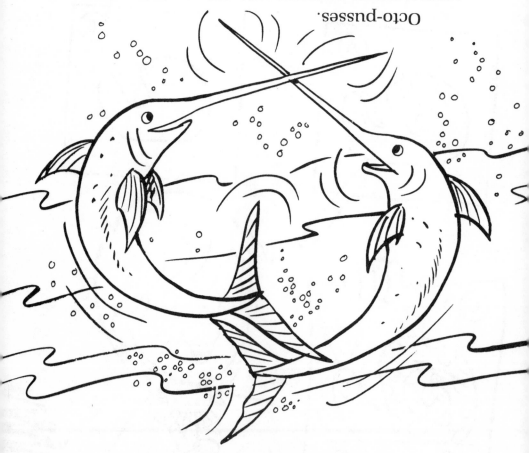

What kind of fish fight duels?

Swordfish.

Why did the skindiver swim so fast?
He did it on porpoise.

What kind of fish come out only at night?
Starfish.

What do you get when you mix an electric eel with a shark?
An electric shark!

Why did the circus animal trainer take his whip to sea?
He wanted to train sea lions and tiger sharks.

When is a crab like a cranky king?
When it's a king crab.

What kind of fish goes with peanut butter?
Jellyfish.

Help the Barracuda

The barracuda on page 15 wants to swim to the top of the sea, but there's a big net in its way. However, the barracuda can cut through a strand in the net with one bite of its sharp teeth.

See if you can help the barracuda out. Start at the bottom and find the strands the barracuda should bite so that it can get to the top *with the least number of cuts.* You cannot cut through a dot.

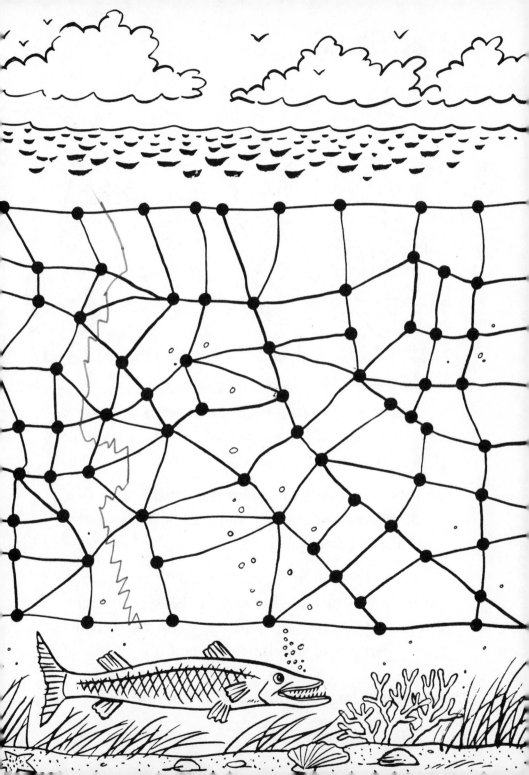

Play "Shark"

You can play this card game with three or more friends. All you need is a deck of regular playing cards.

First remove all the aces from the deck of cards except for the ace of spades. This card will be "the Shark."

One player then deals the cards around until they're all given away. (It doesn't matter if one player ends up with an extra card in his hand.) Someone will have the ace of spades, of course: the Shark! The object of the game is *not* to get caught holding it at the end.

(continued next page)

How to play "Shark"

After the cards have been dealt, each player looks at his hand to find matching pairs — two cards of the same value (two kings, two tens, two threes, etc.). Each player puts the matching pairs on the table faceup. The rest of the cards are held like a fan with the backs facing the other players.

Now the Shark danger begins. Starting with the dealer, each player in turn chooses one card from the hand of the player to his left. If the card matches one in his hand, the player puts the matching pair on the table. If the card doesn't match, the player adds it to his hand.

The game continues until all the players except one have no cards left in their hands. That player, of course, will have the ace of spades — and end up holding the Shark!

Fishy Puzzles

1. Take eight toothpicks (or straws) and form the shape of an angelfish swimming toward the left as shown below. Now here's the puzzle:

   Can you move just three toothpicks so that the angelfish will swim in the opposite direction, toward the right?

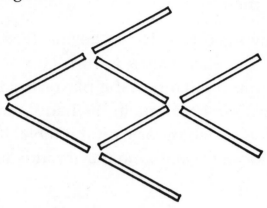

2. Here's another swimming puzzle:

   One of the fish in the circles below is swimming in the opposite direction of the other three. Which one is it?

(more on page 19)

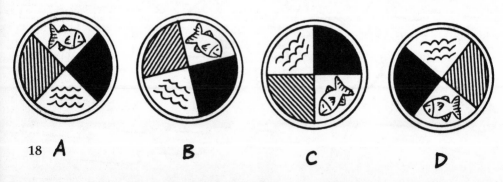

18 A   B   C   D

3. The picture below shows electric eels twirling around in the water. It looks as if there are *two* eels — but there are really *three*. Without tracing them with a pencil, can you tell which drawing is made up of two eels and which is only one?

4. Here's a pyramid of seashells. You can turn it upside down by moving just three shells. Which three shells will do the trick?

Killer Whale!

What steps should you take if a killer whale comes after you?

On each numbered line below, there is one letter that is different from the rest. Put that letter in the box below with the same number, and you will get your answer.

1. h h h h h b h h h
2. 1 1 1 1 1 1 1 i 1
3. q q q q q q q q q
4. a a a a o a a a a
5. m m m m m m n m m
6. c c e c c c c c c
7. z z z z z z z s z

b i g   o n e s !
1 2 3   4 5 6 7

Hidden Sharks

There are six hidden sharks in the picture. Can you find them all?

Wake Up the Octopus

This octopus moves his arms as he wakes up at the bottom of the sea. To watch him do this, follow the instructions on the next page.

1. First cut out the octopus on page 22 along the outline.

2. Starting from the left arm, carefully fold each arm one over the other on the dotted lines as shown in drawings A and B. Press the folds flat. The octopus is now asleep.

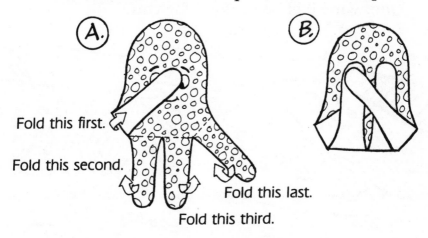

Fold this first.

Fold this second.

Fold this third.

Fold this last.

3. Take a soup plate and fill it with water. Place the octopus so it floats on *top* of the water. In a few seconds the arms will start to unfold one by one, and it will look as if the octopus is alive and waking up!

Did you notice? This "octopus" has only four arms. A real octopus has eight!

Mystery Creature

Who is the mystery creature? To find out, you have to unscramble the five mixed-up words below. Write the correct words on the blank lines. The letters in the circles will then spell out the name of the mystery creature. (One word has been done for you.)

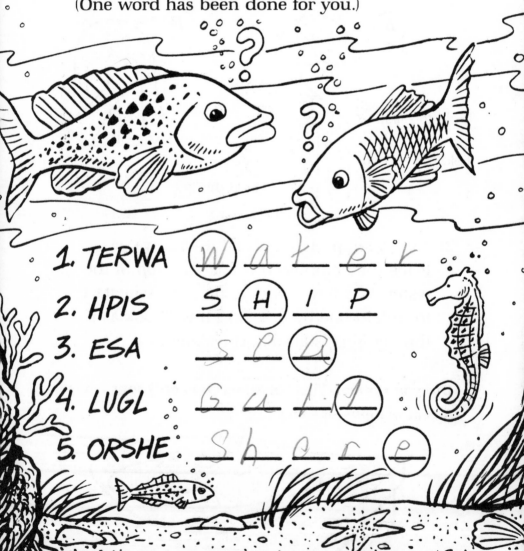

1. TERWA   (W) a t e r

2. HPIS   S (H) I P

3. ESA   S e (a)

4. LUGL   G u l (l)

5. ORSHE   S h o r (e)

Jellyfish Maze

Find your way from IN to OUT without crossing a line.

IN

OUT

Sea Creatures Word Find Puzzle

In the Word Find Puzzle below are hidden the names of ten sea creatures. You can go UP, DOWN, DIAGONALLY, and HORIZONTALLY. When you find the name of a sea creature, circle it with a pencil line.

Look for: SWORDFISH, DOLPHIN, WHALE, EEL, SAILFISH, CRAB, LOBSTER, OCTOPUS, SEA HORSE, and SHARK.

```
A W H A L A I S N S B E R C
S S W O R D F I S H A K A K
W B A E L L H H U A R L R E
O A A I W P E P U R D A L A
R O R R L E O I N P H S C E
D S C O C T O P U S S R E L
F A D O C U I L A E H L E L
I I D O L P I I N A A H S O
S L I B L O L A S H R A R B
T F A O D F I S W O P E A S
E I D H I S F T C R A S H T
R I S S S B C N U S H H A E
E S H O L O B S T E R A E E
I H S I F L O B S T A R S R
```

Undersea Diorama

An underwater scene in a shoe box! You can make it yourself.

1. First, find a shoe box (you don't need the cover) that's about $11\frac{1}{2}$ inches long and $5\frac{3}{4}$ inches deep. (Women's shoes come in boxes this size.)

2. Cut out pages 29 and 31 along the black outlines. Carefully match the scenes and tape them together with clear tape from the back, as shown in drawing A. This will be your diorama background. Color the background with colored pencils or crayons.

3. Place the background inside the shoe box and tape it to the bottom of the box, letting it curve at the sides as shown in drawing B.

See the next page for more instructions.

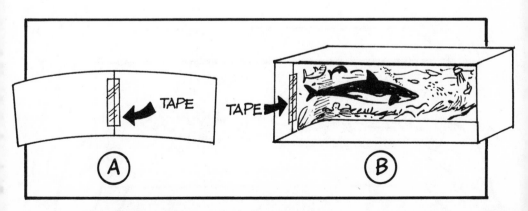

4. Cut out the sea animals
   on page 33 along the black
   outlines, and color them.
   Cut out three pieces of black
   thread each about 5 inches
   long and tape them to the
   back of each animal,
   forming a loop as shown.

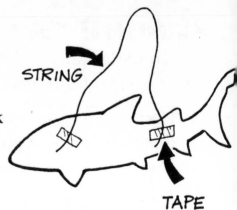

STRING

TAPE

BACK VIEW

5. Tape the top of the loops to the top of the
   box so that the sea animals will "float" in
   the air, as shown in drawing D. Your
   diorama is finished. To watch the animals
   "swim," jiggle the box back and forth.

Note: To make your diorama look something
like an aquarium, tape some plastic wrap over
the front of the box.

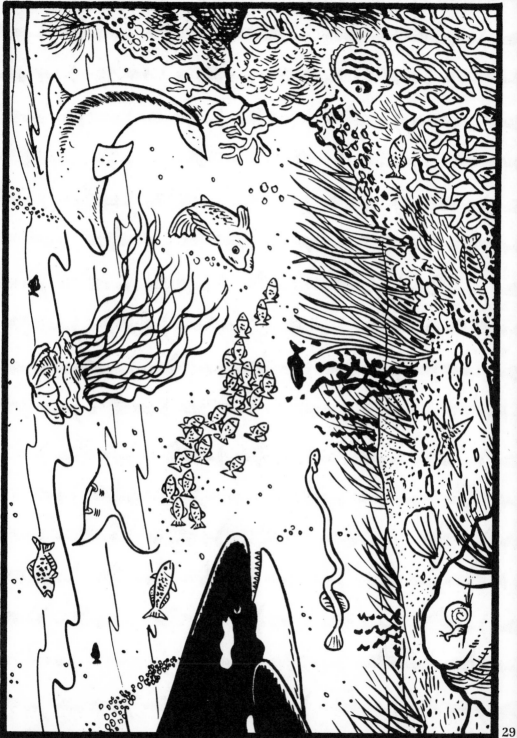

29

Why are these fish swimming away so fast?
Hold the page up to a strong light and you'll
see!

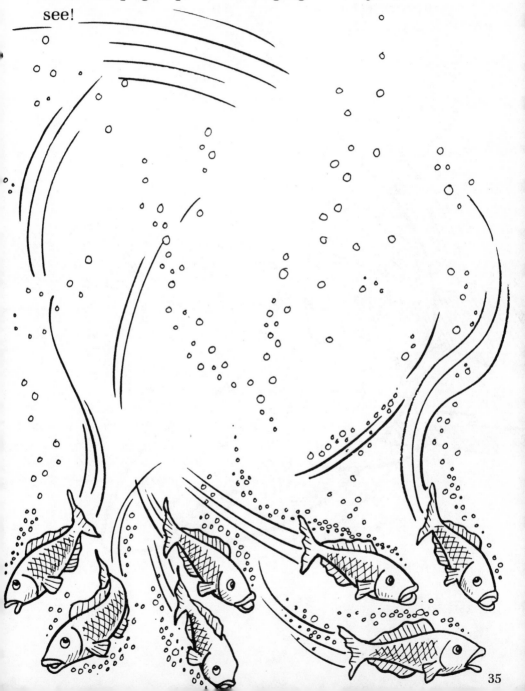

What's going on here? Turn to page 35 to find out.

Follow the Fish

Begin at START and follow the bubbles to FINISH so that you pass each fish along the way. You cannot, however, pass by the same fish twice.

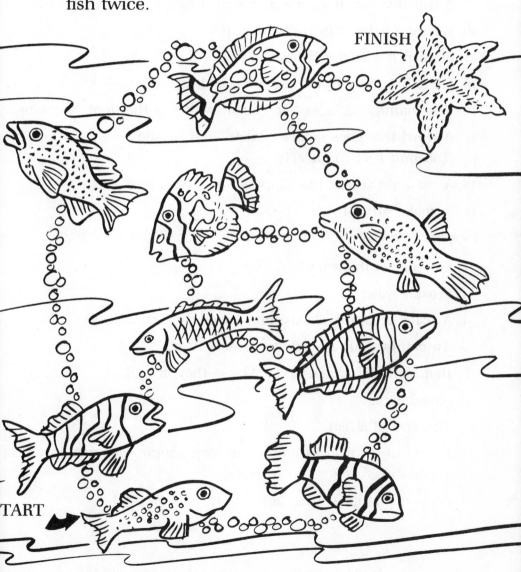

FINISH

START

Starfish Crossword

ACROSS

2. The largest mammal in the world is a whale.

5. The number of arms a starfish has. 5

7. A fish that has the same name as a funny circus performer.

10. Where a fisherman puts a worm.

11. Starfish live at the bottom of the sea.

12. Something fishermen use to catch lots of fish.

16. The manta _ _ _ is a large fish with fins that look like wings.

17. A word that goes before "dollar" and "castle".
    (You find it at the beach.)

18. A sea animal that has flippers and likes to eat fish.

19. A snakelike fish.

DOWN

1. The star of this puzzle.

3. Frozen water.

4. A scary creature. (There may be one in Loch Ness.)

6. An octopus squirts this to protect itself.

8. Hammerhead, Tiger, Great White—they are all _ _ _ _ _ _ _ .

9. "Heigh _ _!"

13. The end of a fish.

14. A kind of tropical fish, or something people may put on top of a Christmas tree.

15. A word that goes after "jelly," "cat," and "sword."

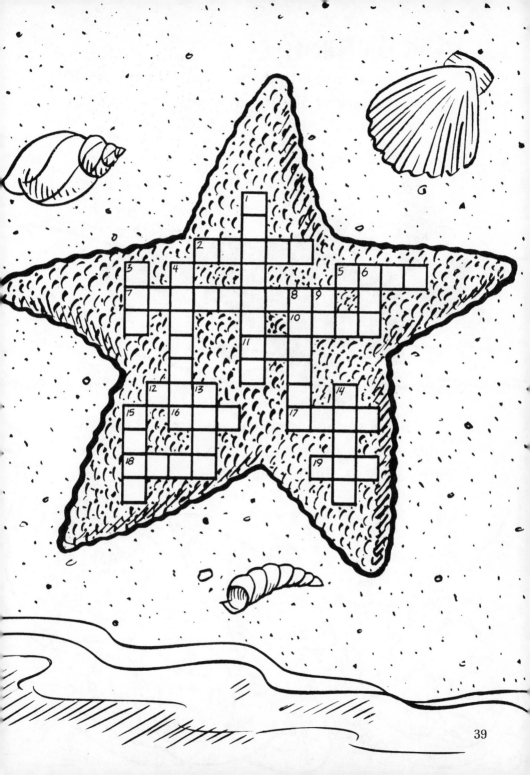

39

Did You Know?

Did you know that the whale shark is the biggest shark of all? It can grow to be 60 feet long and can weigh as much as 15 tons!

Did you know that the giant squid has the biggest eyes of any animal in the world? They are as big as dinner plates!

Did you know that at mating time the male king crab shakes hands with the female? Not only that, but he may shake hands for two to three weeks without stopping!

Did you know that a swordfish uses its sword to catch fish but it doesn't spear them? It beats a fish with the sword until it is dead and then has the fish for dinner!

Answers

Page 3 — A-Mazing Shark

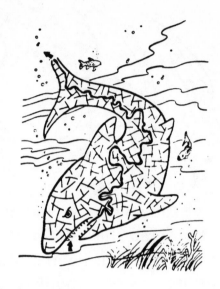

Page 4—The letters spell GOLDFISH

Pages 14 – 15 — Help the Barracuda

The Barracuda can escape in eight bites.

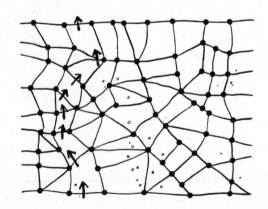

Pages 18 – 19 — Fishy Puzzles

1.

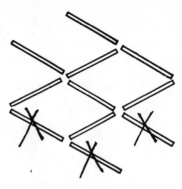

2. The fish in Circle C.

3. Figure A shows one eel and figure B shows two eels. If you don't believe it, fill them in with a pencil.

4.

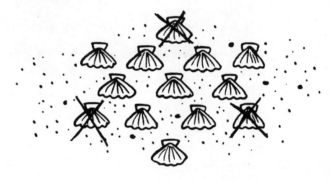

Page 20 — Killer Whale

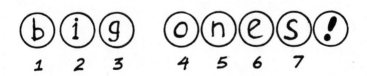

Page 24 — Mystery Creature

1. **W** A T E R
2. S **H** I P
3. S E **A**
4. G U L **L**
5. S H O R **E**

Page 25 — Jellyfish Maze

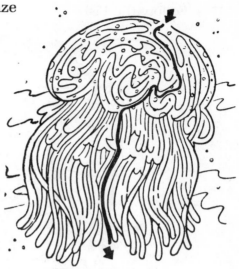

Page 26 — Sea Creatures Word Find

```
A W H A L A I S N S B E R C
S S W O R D F I S H A K A K
W B A E L L H H U A R L R E
O A A I W P E P U R D A L A
R O R R L E O I N P H S C E
D S C O C T O P U S S R E L
F A D O C U I L A E H L E L
I I D O L P I I N A A H S O
S L I B L O L A S H R A R B
T F A O D F I S W O P E A S
E I D H I S F T C R A S H T
R I S S S B C N U S H H A E
E S H O L O B S T E R A E E
I H S I F L O B S T A R S R
```

Page 37 — Follow the Fish

Pages 38 – 39 — Starfish Crossword

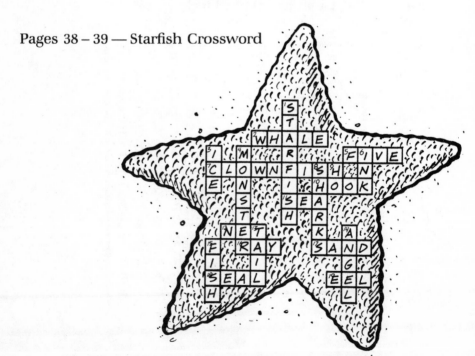